Hide and seek

What can you see?
Some things do not belong in the bathroom.
Find them, then mark them with a cross **X**.

Teddy's bedtime

Look at the pictures.
Number them in the correct order, then tell the story.

1 2 3 4

① 2 3 4

1 2 3 4

1 2 3 4

At the seaside

Look at the two pictures.
Put a cross ✗ on six things that are different.

Colour the flowers

 red

 yellow

 blue

 orange

 pink

6

Which two go together?

Draw a line from each little picture to the correct big picture.

Is it living?

Draw a cross ✗ on five living things.
Draw a ring ◯ around five non-living things.

Colour the teddies

Colour the large teddies to match these small ones.

purple

blue

yellow

pink

orange

brown

red

yellow

A rainy day

Draw a ring round the things Kamal needs to keep himself dry.

Tell the story

Look at the pictures.
Number them in the correct order, then tell the story.

1 2 3

(1) 2 3

1 2 3

1 2 3

1 2 3

1 2 3

What happened first?

Draw a line ———✏ to what came before.

Tell the stories of the pictures.

In the country

Look at the two pictures.
Put a cross ✗ on six things that are different.

Tell the story

Look at the pictures.
Number them in the correct order, then tell the story.

| 1 | 2 | 3 |

| 1 | 2 | 3 |

| 1 | 2 | 3 |

| 1 | 2 | 3 |

| 1 | 2 | 3 |

| 1 | 2 | 3 |

What happened first?

Draw a line  to what came before.

Tell the stories of the pictures.

At the market

Count the vegetables.
Colour the correct number of squares for each vegetable.

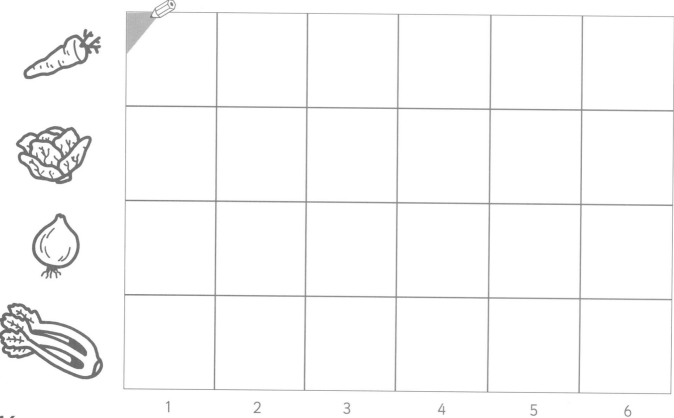

What do I look like?

Make them look the same.

Tell the story

Look at the pictures.
Number them in the correct order, then tell the story.

1   2   3

1   2   3

1   2   3

1   2   3

1   2   3

1   2   3

What happened first?

Draw a line  to what came before.

Tell the stories of the pictures.

Same and different

Make Sophie the same as Polly.

Polly   Sophie

Make Ivan different from Jacob.

Jacob   Ivan

How can they help?

Draw a line from the people to the correct picture.

What happened first?

Draw a line  to what came before.

Tell the stories of the pictures.

On the road

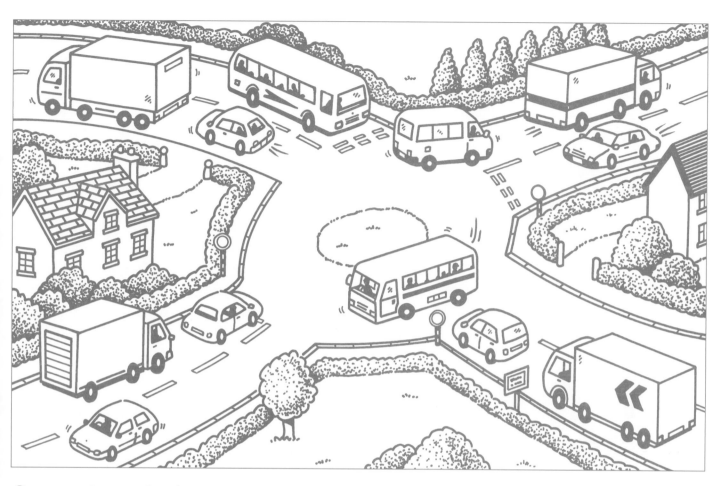

Count the vehicles.
Colour the correct number of squares for each vehicle.

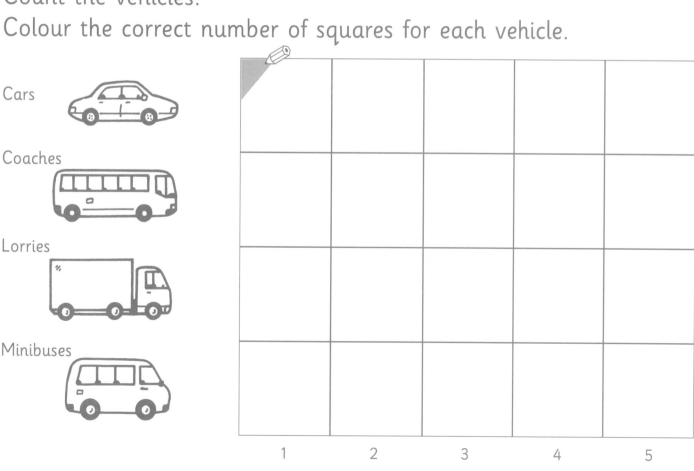

| | 1 | 2 | 3 | 4 | 5 |

Finish the story

Tell the story in the pictures.
What happens next? Draw the picture.

1	2	3

Speech bubble in picture 2: "Ha, ha, hee, hee!"

Read the words. Match to the correct picture.
Write the words.

The cat and the

 spoon

The cow jumped over the

fiddle

The dish ran away with the

 moon

What happens next?

Look at the first two pictures.
Now tick ✔ the picture which shows what
happens next.

or

or

Land or water?

How do you travel – on land or on water?
Match the pictures to where they belong – **land** or **water**.
Write the words.

ship car bike

bus land yacht

water rowing

lifeboat boat

train

Finish the story

Tell the story in the pictures.
What happens next? Draw the picture.

1

2

3

Read the words. Match to the correct picture.
Write the words.

Humpty Dumpty
sat on a

fall

wall

All the king's horses
and all the

king's men

Humpty Dumpty had
a great

27

Where does it belong?

Draw a line from the toys to the toy box.
Draw a line from the large playthings to the playground.

Finish the story

Tell the story in the pictures.
What happens next? Draw the picture.

Read the words. Match to the correct picture.
Write the words.

crown

Jack and Jill
went up the

hill

To fetch a pail of

water

Jack fell down and broke his

29

Underwater

Draw the patterns on the fish in the tank, so they match these.

What happens next?

Look at the first two pictures.
Now tick ✔ the picture which shows what
happens next.

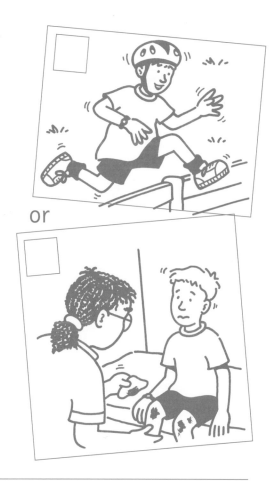

or

or

Schofield & Sims

the long-established educational publisher
specialising in maths, English and science materials for schools

Early Comprehension is a series of graded activity books that develop children's ability to make sense of pictures and text – through activities such as story sequencing, reading for meaning and traditional comprehension work.

Early Comprehension Book 1 covers:

- what happens first/before/next?
- telling a story based on a set of pictures
- reading captions
- identifying how a story ends.

The full range of titles in the series is as follows:

Early Comprehension Book 1:	ISBN 978 07217 0917 8
Early Comprehension Book 2:	ISBN 978 07217 0918 5
Early Comprehension Book 3:	ISBN 978 07217 0950 5

Have you tried **Pre-reading Skills** by Schofield & Sims?
In this series, **Scamp the dog** helps children to make sense of print by looking at picture cues and by sequencing stories.

**For further information and to place your order
visit www.schofieldandsims.co.uk or telephone 01484 607080**

First edition copyright © Schofield and Sims Ltd, 2003
Eleventh impression 2012
Authors: Anne Forster and Paul Martin

Printed in the UK by Wyndeham Gait Ltd, Grimsby, Lincolnshire

ISBN 978-07217-0917-8

9 780721 709178

ISBN 978 07217 0917 8

**£2.45
(Retail price)**

Schofield & Sims

Dogley Mill, Fenay Bridge, Huddersfield HD8 0NQ
Phone: 01484 607080 Facsimile: 01484 606815
E-mail: sales@schofieldandsims.co.uk

Key Stage 1
Age range: 5–7 years